FORESTRY COMMISSION
FIELD BOOK 12

Assessment of
Tree Condition

J. L. Innes
Forestry Commission

LONDON: HMSO

ISBN 0 11 710283 0
ODC 425·1 : 423·1 : 181·45 : 524·6 : (4)

Keywords: *Tree health, Pollution, Forestry*

Enquiries relating to this publication
should be addressed to:
The Technical Publications Officer,
Forestry Commission, Forest Research Station,
Alice Holt Lodge, Wrecclesham,
Farnham, Surrey GU10 4LH

Front cover Healthy Sitka spruce.   *Inset* Sitka spruce with 90% reduction in crown density.

Contents

Assessment of Tree Condition

Summary

Forest condition is now assessed annually in most European countries. This Field Book provides details of assessment procedures used by the Forestry Commission in their main monitoring programme. Although this programme is restricted to Sitka spruce, Norway spruce, Scots pine, oak and beech, the techniques that are described are applicable with little or no modification to most other tree species. Crown density indices for the main conifers (*Larix kaempferi, Picea abies, Picea sitchensis, Pinus contorta, Pinus sylvestris* and *Pseudotsuga menziesii*) and broadleaves (*Acer pseudoplatanus, Betula* spp., *Fagus sylvatica, Fraxinus excelsior, Populus* spp., *Quercus* spp., *Ulmus* spp.) grown in Britain's forests are illustrated in a sequence of colour photographs (five photographs for each species).

While emphasis has been placed on the assessment of crown density, a variety of other indices are also used. These are described and an assessment system is provided for each parameter. The additional indices enable a full description to be made of the condition of a tree.

Évaluation de la Condition des Arbres

Sommaire

À l'heure actuelle on évalue la condition des forêts annuellement dans la plupart des pays d'Europe. Ce Livre de Campagne présente des détails sur les procédés d'évaluation utilisés par la Forestry Commission dans leur programme principal de monitoring. Bien que ce programme se limite à l'épicéa Sitka, l'épicéa commun, le pin sylvestre, le chêne et l'hêtre, les techniques ici décrites sont aussi applicables avec peu ou point de modification à la plupart des autres essences. Pour les essences résineuses principales (*Larix kaempferi, Picea abies, Picea sitchensis, Pinus contorta, Pinus sylvestris* et *Pseudotsuga menziesii*) et les essences feuillues (*Acer pseudoplatanus, Betula* spp., *Fagus sylvatica, Fraxinus excelsior, Populus* spp., *Quercus* spp., *Ulmus* spp.) qui croissent dans les forêts dans Le Royaume-Uni, on illustre les indices de la densité des couronnes dans une serie des photographies en couleur (cinq photographies pour chaque essence).

En même temps qu'on appuye sur l'évaluation de la densité des couronnes, on utilise aussi des autres indices divers. On décrit ces indices, et on présente un système d'évaluation pour chaque paramètre. Les indices additionnels permettent une description complète de la condition de l'arbre.

Baumzustandseinschätzung

Zusammenfassung

Der Waldzustand wird jetzt in den meisten Ländern in Europa jährlich eingeschätzt. Dieses Feldbuch beschreibt die Einzelheiten der Einschätzungsverfahren, die beim Forestry Commission in seinem Hauptmonitoringprogramm benutzt werden. Obgleich das Programm auf Sitkafichte, gemeine Fichte, Kiefer, Eiche und Buche beschränkt ist, sind die hier beschriebenen Verfahren mit weniger oder keiner Änderung auf die meisten anderen Baumarten anwendbar. Für die Hauptnadelhölzer (*Larix kaempferi*, *Picea abies*, *Picea sitchensis*, *Pinus contorta*, *Pinus sylvestris* und *Pseudotsuga menziesii*) und Hauptlaubhölzer (*Acer pseudoplatanus*, *Betula* spp., *Fagus sylvatica*, *Fraxinus excelsior*, *Populus* spp., *Quercus* spp., *Ulmus* spp.), die im Wald in Grossbritannien wachsen, werden Kennziffern der Kronendichte in einer Reihenfolge von Farbbildern (fünf Farbbild für jede Baumart) veranschaulicht.

Wenn auch der Schwerpunkt auf Kronendichteeinschätzung liegt, werden verschiedene andere Kennziffern auch benutzt. Diese Kennziffern werden beschrieben, und ein Einschät-zungssystem für jeden Parameter wird dargestellt. Die zusätzlichen Kennziffern ermöglichen eine ausführliche Beschreiburg des Baumzustandes.

Оценка состояния деревьев

Реферат

В большей части европейских стран оценка состояния леса проводится сейчас ежегодно. Эта полевая книга представляет подробные сведения об оценочных методах, употребляемых Лесной Комиссией в её главной программе мониторинга. Хотя эта программа ограничивается елью ситхинской, елью обыкновенной, сосной обыкновенной, дубом и буком, описанные технические приёмы можно применять к большей части других древесных видов с маленькими модификациями или без модификаций. Показатели сомкнутости кроны для главных хвойных пород (*Larix kaempferi, Picea abies, Picea sitchensis, Pinus contorta, Pinus sylvestris* и *Pseudotsuga menziesii*) и лиственных пород (*Acer pseudoplatanus, Betula* spp., *Fagus sylvatica, Fraxinus excelsior, Populus* spp., *Quercus* spp., *Ulmus* spp.), выращиваемых в лесах Великобритании, иллюстрированы в ряде цветных снимков (пять снимков на каждый вид).

В то время как уделяется особое внимание оценке сомкнутости кроны, употребляется тоже несколько других показателей. Эти описываются, и представляется система оценки для каждого параметра. Эти добавочные показатели способствуют полному описанию состояния дерева.

Assessment of Tree Condition

J. L. Innes, *Forestry Commission*

Introduction

During the 1980s, increasing concern about the state of the environment and its influence on tree health resulted in the establishment of surveys of tree condition throughout Europe. These surveys are conducted on either a national basis or under the auspices of the United Nations Economic Commission for Europe and the Commission of the European Community. Both of the latter organisations have issued guidelines which have been periodically revised as more information has been collected. In most countries, the surveys have developed into complex monitoring programmes, often linked to the monitoring of air quality and other environmental parameters. This Field Book provides information on how such monitoring programmes can be developed to include a range of indices of tree condition.

The aim of this Field Book is to provide guidelines for the establishment and assessment of plots for monitoring the condition of trees mainly using visual features observable from the ground with binoculars. Although particular emphasis is placed on crown density, the Field Book also provides guidelines for the examination of other indices of tree condition. Extensive reference has been made to existing techniques. The intention is not to replace these techniques or standards; rather, there is a need to develop the existing scheme in such a way as to ensure continuity and consistency from year to year. The Field Book is based on a similar guide produced in Switzerland (Bosshard, 1986) which provides photographic standards for trees commonly found in central Europe. Assessment techniques are based on recommendations made in a number of publications which have been listed under 'Further Reading'.

The Field Book is not a guide to pest, disease or other problems affecting trees. A number of guides already exist for this subject area and also have been listed as 'Further Reading'. In Britain, additional advice can be sought from the Pathology and Entomology Branches of the Forestry Commission's Research Division at Alice Holt Lodge (Farnham, Surrey) and the Northern Research Station (Roslin, Midlothian).

Survey design

European surveys have used a systematic sampling design, based on a fixed grid. The scale has varied from 1 × 1 km in the Netherlands, to 16 × 16 km in most other countries. The scale adopted depends on the extent of forest cover and the nature and severity of the problem being investigated. For example, in the long term, it may be advantageous to establish a dense sampling network initially and then use a less dense network for monitoring. Suitable sampling intervals for such a scheme are 1, 2, 4, 8, 12 and 16 km. Normally, plots are only located where grid intersections fall in forest. However, a variant of this approach is to establish a plot in woodland close to the intersection, if the intersection falls outside woodland. This should be done using an objective procedure such as a random selection from a more detailed grid overlaying the area in question. One advantage of this approach is that an even coverage of plots across the survey area will be achieved, regardless of woodland density.

A systematic sampling design is not always the most useful approach. A variety of other designs exist and, for studies of forest condition, two appear to be particularly useful. The first is a transect across the area in question or along a gradient in the environmental stress being investigated. The second is a stratified random sampling design. Strata can be defined to include only those stands or tree species that are of interest. This is usually the most cost-effective method of sampling.

In all cases, trees within stands should be selected using a strictly defined procedure. The most widely adopted method is known as the cross-cluster. The centre of the cross is located at an exact grid point and trees are located at a set distance (usually 25 m) from the centre at each of the cardinal points of the compass (Figure 1). In very dense stands, it may be necessary to extend the arms of the cross to a position where the crowns of the target trees are readily visible from the ground. In either case, a set number of trees is located at each of the four sampling points, usually on the basis of the six closest trees that fulfil certain requirements (defined at the start of the survey).

Usual practice is to examine 24 trees in each stand. Statistically, a sample size of 40 provides more reliable estimates of stand characteristics in even-aged, single-species plantations, and this should be seen as a preferable sample size. However, the benefits of an increase in sample size must be offset against the cost of the work. As a rough guide, the full assessment of a tree (using the indices described below) takes about 5–8 minutes, depending on the condition of the tree. When uneven-aged, mixed species stands are being investigated, 24 trees are insufficient to adequately characterise the stand, and a minimum sample size of 40 is essential.

It is useful to make notes about the location of the trees and the site. The presence of any management activities (such as thinning) should be recorded as should the position of each sub-plot in relation to other trees, the edge of the stand and the edge of the forest. In addition, any factors that might have influenced the condition of the trees should be recorded, including details of soil type, slope, drainage, etc.

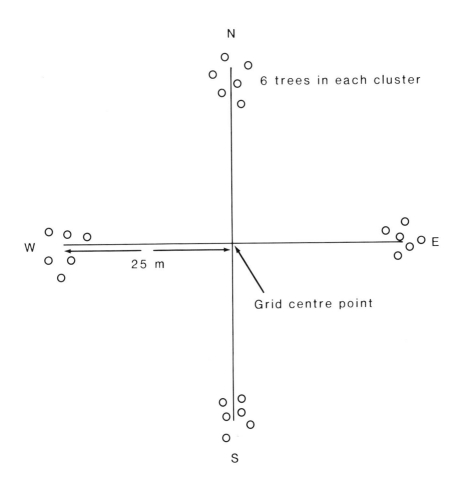

Figure 1. Location of trees at a sampling point.

3

Individual tree assessments

A variety of parameters can be assessed for each tree and the ones that are selected will depend on the aims of the investigation. In each case, the scoring system used by the Forestry Commission in its monitoring programme is given. These should not be seen as rigid and, for specific investigations, more detailed scoring systems for particular indices may be desirable. The scoring systems described on the following pages have been tested in the field and found to be practical.

The Forestry Commission monitoring programme is restricted to five species: Sitka spruce, Norway spruce, Scots pine, oak and beech. Consequently, many of the scoring systems outlined here are specifically designed for these species. However, experience has indicated that most can be easily adapted to other species, although the detailed assessment of deciduous conifers, such as larch, presents a problem. For the crown density standards, a variety of species have been shown, as the health survey undertaken for the European Community, which relies heavily on assessments of crown density, is not restricted to the five species used in the main British monitoring programme.

For each tree, it is important to ensure that a good view of the crown is available. This is normally achieved by standing about one tree length away but, in closed canopies, this may not be practical and the consequent loss of accuracy should be taken into account. Looking upwards from directly underneath the tree produces a particularly misleading view of the tree.

Most of the assessments involve a subjective evaluation of a particular feature. Variation between observers can be successfully reduced through comprehensive on-site training (Innes, 1988). When such training is unavailable, observers should try to examine trees in a range of conditions before undertaking any formal survey. This will help reduce errors due to inexperience.

The scoring systems described in this Field Book are based on the presence of particular aspects of crown condition. If a feature is absent, the tree is usually scored as zero. If a feature type is not on the list of options, it is scored as 'other', and the observer is asked to describe the feature in question.

Scoring systems

Tree measurements

A variety of measurements can be made of the physical attributes of the tree. These include diameter at breast height (1·3 m above ground), tree height, crown length (measured from the base of the crown to the top of the tree) and crown diameter. Of these, diameter at breast height is the most accurate; the other measurements can be subject to considerable error, particularly in broadleaved trees, unless sophisticated instrumentation is available.

Tree dominance

Four classes are recognised:
1: dominant – trees with the upper crown standing above the general level of the canopy;
2: co-dominant – trees with crowns forming the general level of the canopy;
3: intermediate – trees extending into the canopy and receiving some light from above, but shorter than 1 or 2;
4: suppressed – trees with crowns below the general level of the canopy, receiving no direct light from above.

In most studies, trees in class 4 are excluded from the assessments.

Canopy closure

Canopy closure provides a measure of the openness of the tree's situation. Open-grown trees usually have much larger crowns than ones in closed canopies and this affects some of the other indices. It is assessed on a five-point scale as follows:
0: crown open-grown or with no evidence of shading effects;
1: crown in contact with others on one side;
2: crown in contact with others on two sides;
3: crown in contact with others on three sides;
4: crown in contact with others on four sides.

Branch density in conifers

The relatively fast rate of growth of many conifers in Britain compared with the same species in continental Europe is one of the reasons why many apparently have thin crowns. It is useful to record the branching density as this may explain some or all of a crown thinness score. However, branch density is extremely difficult to estimate accurately as its influence varies according to crown pattern. An approximate system has been developed, based on estimates of the amount of trunk that would have been visible had the tree been fully needled. The categories are:

1: dense branching with the stem totally obscured;
2: small parts of the stem visible (<20 cm in any one place);
3: large parts of stem visible;
4: stem visible throughout the crown.

Branch pattern in spruce

In spruce, several branch types can be recognised. In some cases, more than one type may occur on the same tree, with the gradation usually occurring vertically. Three types appear to be particularly common. They are scored as:

1: comb;
2: brush and/or plate;
3: hanging brush;
4: mixture of more than one type.

The different forms are shown in Figures 2a–2c. The brush and plate types have been combined into a single category as many trees appear to be intermediate between the two.

a.

b.

c.

Figure 2. Branch types in spruce.
a. comb (1)
b. brush/plate (2)
c. hanging brush (3).

Defoliation type in spruce

Six types of defoliation have been recognised in spruce. These vary in their frequency, with some (such as peripheral defoliation) being very rare in Britain. The following types are distinguished (Westman and Lesinski, 1986):

1: small window in the upper crown, caused by shoot or branch loss (sub-top dying);
2: large window, extending into the lower crown;
3: death of the uppermost branches and leader (top-dying);
4: uniform loss of needles throughout the crown giving an overall thinness (larch-type defoliation);
5: loss of needles and shoots at the extremities of the branches (peripheral defoliation);
6: loss of needles from the base of the crown upwards.

They are illustrated schematically in Figure 3.

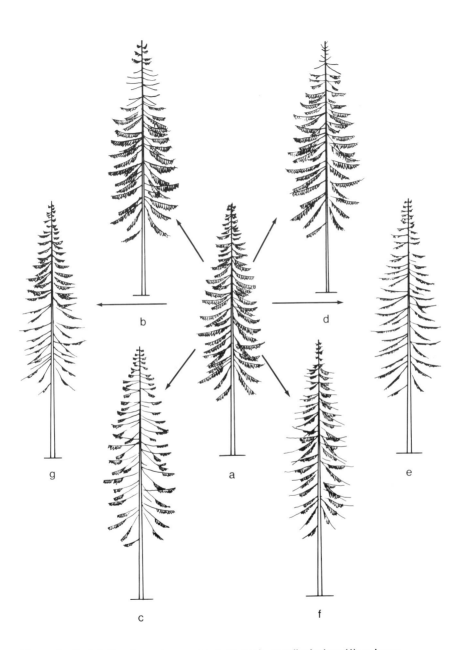

Figure 3. Defoliation types in spruce. a. none; b. small window (1); c. large window (2); d. top only (3); e. uniform (4); f. peripheral (5); g. bottom-up (6).

9

Defoliation type in pine

As with spruce species, a number of different defoliation types can be recognised (Lesinski and Landmann, 1988):

1: defoliation of lower crown;
2: peripheral defoliation;
3: gap-like defoliation, with either occasional thinly-needled or dead branches within the crown or missing branches;
4: uniform loss of needles throughout the crown;
5: spot-like defoliation, with occasional branches with full needle complements, but the majority being thinly-needled;
6: defoliation of upper crown.

Various types of defoliation are shown in Figure 4.

a.　　　　　　b.　　　　　　c.

d.　　　　　e.

Figure 4. Defoliation types in pine.
a. lower crown only (1)
b. gap-like (3)
c. uniform (4)
d. spot-like (5)
e. upper crown (6).

10

Defoliation type in broadleaves

Crown density can be useful as a measure of tree vigour, but recent work has suggested that other measures may be equally or even more important. One such is crown pattern, which indicates the extent of break-up of the crown. Practice has indicated that it is usually impossible to categorise a tree with less than 20% leaf loss and this figure should be used as a threshold for looking at crown pattern. The following classes have been recognised (Westman, 1989):

0: less than 20% loss of density;
1: no clear pattern;
2: small gaps, with all or part of the crown transparent as a result of many small spaces caused by sparse foliage;
3: gaps in the lateral branch system, but less than 50% loss of crown density;
4: large gaps in lateral branch system, main branches being more-or-less bare almost to the ends of the branches;
5: mainly large gaps, with leaves restricted to the shoot tips or to adventitious shoots;
6: whole or part of crown completely defoliated.

The different types are shown in Figure 5.

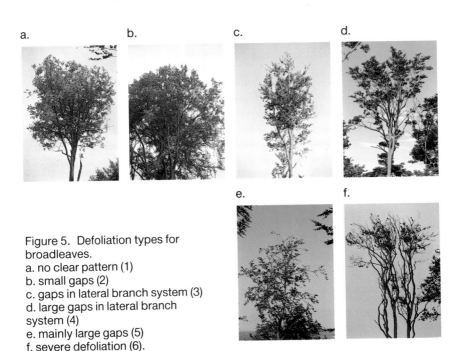

Figure 5. Defoliation types for broadleaves.
a. no clear pattern (1)
b. small gaps (2)
c. gaps in lateral branch system (3)
d. large gaps in lateral branch system (4)
e. mainly large gaps (5)
f. severe defoliation (6).

11

Crown dieback in broadleaves

Several stages of dieback can be identified (Figure 6) and these should be recorded (Westman, 1989):

1: leaf loss only, with lateral branches partly or completely bare;
2: dieback restricted to relatively thin branches;
3: several large branches involved;
4: main stem involved in the upper part of the crown.

The location of the dieback should also be noted:

1: top of the tree only;
2: middle parts of the crown;
3: top and middle;
4: branches at the base of the crown;
5: throughout crown.

An assessment should be made, in 5% classes, of the percentage of the crown affected by dieback, expressed as a percentage of the crown that would have been there if no defoliation or dieback had been present.

a.   b.   c.

d.

Figure 6. Crown dieback
in broadleaves.
a. leaf loss (1)
b. thin branches (2)
c. large branches (3)
d. stem (4).

12

Crown form in broadleaves

Designed initially for beech (Roloff, 1985), this index has been extended to other broadleaved species (Roloff, 1989). Considerable difficulty has been experienced in applying the index. The difficulty arises from problems associated with variation in the scores obtained by different observers and the presence of trees that do not readily fit into the classification. Consequently, it is not recommended for general use, but is included as some scientists have found it useful. In beech, four categories are recognised (Figure 7):

0: trees with vigorous growth of both apical and side shoots;
1: apical shoots still growing vigorously, but side shoots much slower, resulting in the development of 'spears';
2: both side shoots and apical shoots with reduced growth, resulting in the development of 'claws';
3: growth stopped and defoliation and dieback occurring.

a.   b.

c.   d.

Figure 7. Crown form in beech.
a. vigorous growth (0)
b. spear development (1)
c. claw shoots (2)
d. growth stopped (3).

Crown form in pine

As pines get older, the crown form changes from vigorous apical dominance to a flat platform. Observations suggest that under certain types of stress, the loss of apical dominance may occur earlier than usual, and crown form may therefore provide a useful index of the vigour of a tree. Six classes are recognised (Niehaus, 1989):

1: vigorous apical dominance with tree growing strongly upwards;
2: reduced apical dominance with some evidence of flattening;
3: no apical dominance with crown showing signs of widening;
4: as 3, but lower branches being lost through suppression;
5: platform developing, but crown still with some depth;
6: platform fully developed.

The various forms are shown in Figure 8.

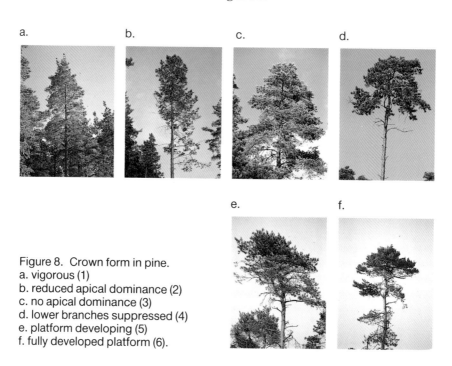

Figure 8. Crown form in pine.
a. vigorous (1)
b. reduced apical dominance (2)
c. no apical dominance (3)
d. lower branches suppressed (4)
e. platform developing (5)
f. fully developed platform (6).

14

Shoot death in spruce and pine

The extent and location of shoot death in the crown provides an important measure of the tree's health. The location within the crown can be divided into six categories:

1: top three branch whorls only;
2: top quarter of the crown;
3: top half of the crown;
4: bottom half of the crown;
5: middle part of the crown only;
6: all over the crown.

The location of the shoot death on individual branches is important for diagnostic purposes. Five positions are recognised:

1: outermost shoots only;
2: shoots on the middle of the branch;
3: innermost parts of branch;
4: middle and inner parts of branch;
5: all over the branch.

These positions refer to the location relative to the main stem. The extent of shoot death is difficult to estimate, and a scale with broad categories has been devised:

1: rare (1–10 dead shoots);
2: scattered (11–50 dead shoots);
3: common (>50 dead shoots, but live shoots more frequent than dead ones);
4: abundant (more dead shoots than live ones).

Secondary shoots in spruce

Secondary shoots develop under a number of circumstances, but they may be particularly obvious on trees that have previously suffered severe defoliation. They are distinguished from normal shoots by their occurrence on the upper surfaces of branches (Figure 9). There can be confusion between normal and secondary shoots and an arbitrary definition of a secondary shoot has been adopted as one growing out of wood that is at least 4 years older than the shoot. Usually, it is very hard to assess their frequency on densely-needled trees, and the Forestry Commission has adopted a threshold of 20% reduction in crown density before secondary shoots are assessed. Their location on branches and frequency are both noted. The following branch locations are recognised:

1: outer parts of branches only;
2: middle of branches;
3: inner parts of branches;
4: outer and middle parts;
5: middle and inner parts;
6: all along the branch.

The frequency of secondary shoots is difficult to assess, but the following categories have been used:

1: a few shoots on less than a quarter of the branches;
2: many shoots on less than a quarter of the branches;
3: a few shoots on many branches;
4: many shoots on many branches, with the shoots making a significant contribution to the crown density of the tree.

Figure 9. Secondary shoots on Norway spruce.

Epicormics in broadleaves

Epicormic or adventitious shoots occur in a variety of species, usually in response to suddenly increased light reaching the stem or branches (Figure 10). They should be assessed separately for the stem and for branches, as the frequency on each may be very different. The following scoring system has been used:

1: rare;
2: scattered (11–50 on the stem or one or two main branches with them);
3: common (51–100 on the stem or several main branches with them);
4: abundant (stem totally obscured by epicormics or majority of main branches with them).

a.   b.

Figure 10. Epicormic shoots on a. oak and b. elm.

Leader condition in conifers

The condition of the leader provides an indication of the future potential for the height growth of the tree. In spruce, seven different forms of damage have been noted:

1: shorter than current-year side shoots;
2: missing;
3: bent or twisted;
4: double;
5: broken;
6: bare;
7: side shoots taken over apical dominance.

A further category is recognised in Scots pine: trees with no apical dominance.

Flowering in pine

Each spring, male flowers may occur (instead of needles) on developing shoots. Towards the end of the summer, needles can be seen on the outermost part of the shoot and an area of bare shoot occurs where the flowers were (Figure 11). The flowering can result in an apparent loss of density and should therefore be recorded. The intensity of flowering is usually much greater in the lower part of the crown than in the upper, and scores for the two halves should be separated. The following scale can be used:

1: rare, 1–10% of branches;
2: infrequent, 11–25% of branches;
3: common, 26–60% of branches;
4: abundant, >60% of branches.

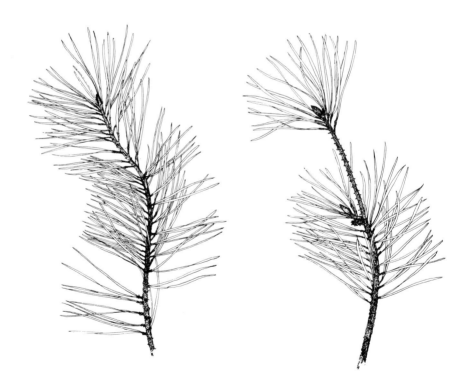

Figure 11. Effect of male flowering on Scots pine.

18

Fruiting

Fruiting occurs in response to a variety of factors, one of which is stress. It is therefore useful to record the presence of any fruiting. As some pines retain their cones for two summers, assessments of coning in pines should be restricted to 2nd year cones (i.e. those about to produce seed). Four broad categories have been identified:

0: none;
1: scarce;
2: common;
3: abundant.

Needle retention

Needle retention is recorded as the age of the oldest needles held by the tree. As this varies within the crown, an average figure is estimated from the uppermost third of the crown; observers should note that any whorl within the top seven cannot hold more than 7 years of needles. Hands-on counts of needle retention on the lower branches may underestimate the average value for the crown. With species that retain their needles for a long time (such as the spruces), counting back may be very difficult, particularly on densely-needled trees. Consequently, trees with more than 7 years' needle retention should be classed as a single group. This avoids the potential underestimation of needle retention in healthy trees.

Needle size

Needle size can vary quite markedly from year to year (Figure 12). If branches in the upper crown can be reached, it is worth recording the average needle length for each year class present in the seventh whorl. Additional measurements, such as needle density per unit shoot length and needle cross-sectional area require more time-consuming laboratory-based studies. Comparisons can be made between year classes on individual trees and between trees.

Figure 12. Variation in the needle size of Scots pine.

Leaf size

On some trees, the leaves are noticeably smaller or larger than normal as compared with the rest of the trees in the stand. If this is the case, it should be recorded.

Discoloration

Discoloration of foliage takes a number of forms. In conifers, the year class should be distinguished, with the minimum requirement being the separation of current needles from older needles. The incidence of necrotic (brown) needles should be recorded separately from chlorotic (yellow) needles (Figure 13). Any other types of discoloration should be recorded. The extent of discoloration is normally assessed in five categories:

0: 0–10% of needles;
1: 11–25% of needles;
2: 26–60% of needles;
3: 61–99% of needles;
4: dead trees.

The uneven categories take into account the difficulty of accurately estimating the proportion of needles affected by discoloration, although for some species it may be possible to use 5 or 10% classes. A variety of different types of discoloration can be noted, although for accurate assessment these require that needles be examined in the hand. For necrotic needles, the following types should be recorded:

1: necrotic tips to needles;
2: necrotic spots on needles;
3: half or more of each needle necrotic;
4: entire needle necrotic.

For chlorotic needles, rather different patterns may be apparent:

1: tree generally showing a yellowish appearance;
2: chlorotic tips to needles;
3: chlorotic flecks or bands;
4: upper surfaces of needles only;
5: entire needles chlorotic.

The position of the discoloration in the crown should be noted (for example, if it is restricted to one side of the tree).

Assessment of discoloration in deciduous broadleaves is easier as only one year class of foliage is present. Necrosis and chlorosis should be separated and the extent of discoloration recorded in the five classes given above. The following types of necrosis can be recorded:

1: leaf margins only;
2: leaf tips only;
3: spots on leaves;
4: scattered leaves entirely brown;
5: occasional shoots with all leaves entirely brown;
6: occasional branches with all leaves entirely brown.

As with the conifers, chlorosis usually takes a slightly different form:

1: leaf margins chlorotic;
2: some shoots or branches chlorotic, the rest of the crown being the normal colour;
3: entire tree yellowish-green;
4: entire tree greenish-yellow;
5: entire tree chlorotic.

a.

b.

c.

d.

Figure 13. Various
different forms of
discoloration.
a. tips necrotic
b. scattered current-year
needles necrotic
c. scattered older
needles necrotic
d. older needles chlorotic
e. necrosis restricted to
one side of tree
f. chlorosis of current
year needles.

e.

f.

Mechanical damage

Tree crowns can be affected by a variety of mechanical forms of damage. The following are recognised in the British programme, although other types undoubtedly occur:

1: abrasion of peripheral shoots;
2: wind and snow damage;
3: prevailing wind effect (lop-sided crown);
4: damage caused by adjacent trees leaning into target tree;
5: hail;
6: lightning;
7: damage to the crown caused by harvesting operations.

Butt and stem damage

Many different forms of butt and stem damage can occur. It is important to record these as they may have a significant effect on the overall condition of the tree:

1: dead area with bark still present;
2: area of exposed wood;
3: resin flow from cracks or holes;
4: swelling (covering over previous damage);
5: crack at least five times long as wide;
6: fungus, i.e. a visible fruiting body on the stem;
7: extraction damage;
8: insect activity (e.g. resin tubes, emergence holes, insects present);
9: tarry spots on bark;
10: vandalism;
11: pruning or brashing wounds;
12: animal damage (e.g. bark stripping);
13: fire.

A note should be made of the age of the damage (fresh or old) and its extent.

Insect damage

There are a number of recognised ways of scoring insect damage. In conifers, it is usually impractical to determine the number of needles affected and fairly broad categories have been adopted:

1: rare, only a few shoots affected;
2: infrequent, less than 50 shoots affected;
3: common, many shoots affected;
4: abundant, most shoots affected.

In broadleaves, it is usually possible to estimate the proportion of leaves affected and the proportion of leaf area lost. If possible, insect damage in both conifers and broadleaves should be separated into damage caused by sucking insects (which mainly takes the form of discoloration and leaf/needle loss) and damage caused by chewing insects (parts or the majority of individual leaves/needles removed).

Fungal damage

In some cases, it may be possible to separate fungal damage from other forms of damage. As with insect damage, the presence/absence of a particular fungus may depend on the time of year of the observation. The proportion of foliage (and, for conifers, the year class affected) should be estimated.

Leaf-rolling

Leaf-rolling occurs in beech in the mid- and late summer (Figure 14). It is also present in other species (such as oak), where it is induced by insect attack. The rolling in beech is little understood, although it is probably a response to some sort of moisture stress. Both the frequency and the degree should be recorded. For frequency of rolling, the following classes have proved useful:

1: leaves on a few shoots in the upper crown;
2: leaves on a few shoots elsewhere in the crown;
3: leaves on about half the shoots in the upper crown;
4: leaves on about half the shoots throughout the crown;
5: leaves on most shoots in the upper crown;
6: leaves on most shoots throughout the crown;
7: virtually all leaves affected.

Several degrees of rolling can be recognised:

1: slightly curved upwards at edges;
2: curled, but not tightly;
3: tightly curled, with sides touching each other.

Figure 14. Examples of leaf-rolling in beech.

Premature leaf loss

Leaves may be lost prematurely as indicated by the presence of green leaves on the ground below trees. It can be scored as:

1: infrequent;
2: common (more than 50 leaves);
3: abundant (carpeting the ground under the tree).

Crown density

Crown density is one of the most widely used indices of tree condition used in forest health surveys. It can be assessed in a number of ways, each with its relative advantages and disadvantages. For long-term monitoring, it is essential to have fixed standards against which trees are compared through time. The only effective way of doing this is to use photographic standards. Photographic standards can also be used to ensure that the same standards are used by different observers in any given year. The following pictures provide such standards for a number of species. Further pictures, showing crown types commonly encountered in central Europe, can be found in Bosshard (1986), which should be used to supplement this Field Book where necessary.

Reductions in crown density should be assessed in 5% classes. The scores represent the amount of light passing through the crown and a high score does not necessarily mean that a tree has lost foliage. Rather, it indicates that it does not have as much foliage as a completely dense tree. Trees with no reduction should be classed separately:

  0: no reduction;
  5: 1–5% reduction;
 10: 6–10% reduction;
 15: 11–15% reduction;
 20: 16–20% reduction;
     and so on.

Conifers

5%

Japanese larch *Larix kaempferi*

25%

Japanese larch *Larix kaempferi*

50%

Japanese larch *Larix kaempferi*

75%

Japanese larch *Larix kaempferi*

90%

Japanese larch *Larix kaempferi*

5%

Norway spruce *Picea abies*

20%

Norway spruce *Picea abies*

35%

Norway spruce *Picea abies*

60%

Norway spruce *Picea abies*

85%

Norway spruce *Picea abies*

0%

Sitka spruce *Picea sitchensis*

25%

Sitka spruce *Picea sitchensis*

45%

Sitka spruce *Picea sitchensis*

80%

Sitka spruce *Picea sitchensis*

90%

Sitka spruce *Picea sitchensis*

0%

Lodgepole pine *Pinus contorta*

25%

Lodgepole pine *Pinus contorta*

40%

Lodgepole pine *Pinus contorta*

70%

Lodgepole pine *Pinus contorta*

90%

Lodgepole pine *Pinus contorta*

0%

Scots pine *Pinus sylvestris*

25%

Scots pine *Pinus sylvestris*

40%

Scots pine *Pinus sylvestris*

70%

Scots pine *Pinus sylvestris*

85%

Scots pine *Pinus sylvestris*

0%

Douglas fir *Pseudotsuga menziesii*

20%

Douglas fir *Pseudotsuga menziesii*

35%

Douglas fir *Pseudotsuga menziesii*

55%

Douglas fir *Pseudotsuga menziesii*

80%

Douglas fir *Pseudotsuga menziesii*

Broadleaves

10%

Sycamore *Acer pseudoplatanus*

30%

Sycamore *Acer pseudoplatanus*

60%

Sycamore *Acer pseudoplatanus*

80%

Sycamore *Acer pseudoplatanus*

95%

Sycamore *Acer pseudoplatanus*

5%

Birch *Betula* spp.

25%

Birch *Betula* spp.

50%

Birch *Betula* spp.

70%

Birch *Betula* spp.

95%

Birch *Betula* spp.

10%

Beech *Fagus sylvatica*

30%

Beech *Fagus sylvatica*

45%

Beech *Fagus sylvatica*

65%

Beech *Fagus sylvatica*

95%

Beech *Fagus sylvatica*

10%

Ash *Fraxinus excelsior*

25%

Ash *Fraxinus excelsior*

40%

Ash *Fraxinus excelsior*

55%

Ash *Fraxinus excelsior*

75%

Ash *Fraxinus excelsior*

10%

Poplar *Populus* spp.

20%

Poplar *Populus* spp.

50%

Poplar *Populus* spp.

70%

Poplar *Populus* spp.

90%

Poplar *Populus* spp.

10%

Oak *Quercus* spp.

30%

Oak *Quercus* spp.

55%

Oak *Quercus* spp.

80%

Oak *Quercus* spp.

95%

Oak *Quercus* spp.

5%

Elm *Ulmus* spp.

35%

Elm *Ulmus* spp.

60%

Elm *Ulmus* spp.

65%

Elm *Ulmus* spp.

90%

Elm *Ulmus* spp.

FURTHER READING

ALEXANDER, S. A. and CARLSON, J. A. (1988). *Visual damage survey pilot plot test project manual.* Virginia Polytechnic Institute and State University, Blacksburg, Virginia.

ANON. (1988). *Diagnosing injury to Eastern forest trees. A manual for identifying damage caused by air pollution, pathogens, insects and abiotic stresses.* National Acid Precipitation Assessment Program, Forest Responses Program, Vegetation Survey Research Cooperative. U.S. Department of Agriculture, Forest Service, Forest Pest Management, Atlanta and The Pennsylvania College of Agriculture, Department of Plant Pathology, University Park, Pennsylvania.

BELANGER, R. P. and ANDERSON, R. L. (1988). *A guide for visually assessing crown densities of loblolly and shortleaf pine.* U.S. Department of Agriculture, Forest Service, South-East Forest Experiment Station Note SE-352, Asheville.

BOSSHARD, W. (ed.) (1986). *Kronenbilder mit Nadel- und Blattverlustprozenten.* Eidgenössische Anstalt für das forstliche Versuchswesen, Birmensdorf.

GRUBER, F. (1989). Phänotypen der Fichte (*Picea abies* (L.) Karst.). I Verzweigungsphänotypen: Genotyp und Modifikation. *Allgemeine Forst- und Jagd-Zeitung* **160**, 157–166.

HARTMANN, G., NIENHAUS, F. and BUTIN, H. (1988). *Farbatlas Waldschäden. Diagnose und Baumkrankheiten.* Eugen Ulmer, Stuttgart.

INNES, J. L. (1988). Forest health surveys: problems in assessing observer objectivity. *Canadian Journal of Forest Research* **18**, 560–565.

INNES, J. L. and BOSWELL, R. C. (1990). Reliability, presentation and relationships amongst data from inventories of forest condition. *Canadian Journal of Forest Research* **20** (6), 790–799.

LESINSKI, J. A. (1989). Dynamics of injury symptoms in Norway spruce. In, *International congress on forest decline research: state of knowledge and perspectives.* Poster Abstracts Vol. 1, 55–56. Forschungsbeirat Waldschäden/Luftverunreinigungen der Bundesregierung und der Länder, Bonn.

LESINSKI, J. A. and LANDMANN, G. (1988). Crown and branch malformation in conifers related to forest decline. In, *Scientific basis of forest decline symptomatology,* eds. J. N. Cape and P. Mathy, 92–105. Commission of the European Communities, Air Pollution Report 15, Brussels.

LESINSKI, J. A. and WESTMAN, L. (1987). Crown injury types in Norway spruce and their applicability for forest inventory. In, *Acid rain: scientific and technical advances*, eds. R. Perry, R. M. Harrison, J. N. B. Bell and J. N. Lester, 657–662. Selper, London.

MAGASI, L. P. (1988). *Acid rain national early warning system. Manual on plot establishment and monitoring.* Canadian Forestry Service Report DPC-X-25. Canadian Forestry Service, Canada.

NIEHAUS, G. (1989). Terrestrische Zustandserfassung von Kiefernkronen (*Pinus sylvestris*) – ein differenzierter Anspracheschlüssel. *Der Forst und Holzwirt* 44, 200–206.

ROLOFF, A. (1985). Schadstufen bei der Buche. *Der Forst und Holzwirt* 40, 131–134.

ROLOFF, A. (1989). Kronenentwicklung und Vitalitätsbeurteilung ausgewählter Baumarten des gemässigten Breiten. *Schriften aus der forstlichen Fakultät der Universität Göttingen* 93.

SINCLAIR, W. A., LYON, H. H. and JOHNSON, W. T. (1987). *Diseases of trees and shrubs.* Cornell University Press, Ithaca.

UN-ECE (1988). *Manual on methodologies and criteria for harmonized sampling, assessment, monitoring and analysis of the effects of air pollution and forests.* United Nations Environment Programme, Geneva.

WESTMAN, L. (1989). A new method for assessment of visible damage to birch and other deciduous trees. In, *Air pollution and forest decline*, eds. J. B. Bucher and I. Bucher-Wallin, 223–228. Eidgenössische Anstalt für das forstliche Versuchswesen, Birmensdorf.

WESTMAN, L. and LESINSKI, J. A. (1986). *Kronutglesning och andra förändringar i grankronan.* Naturvårdsverket Rapport 3262.

Addresses

Forestry Commission, Forest Research Station, Alice Holt Lodge, Wrecclesham, Farnham, Surrey, GU10 4LH.

Forestry Commission, Northern Research Station, Roslin, Midlothian, EH25 9SY.

Printed in the United Kingdom for HMSO
Dd. 291289 C30 8/90